LIFTING AND HANDLING
An Ergonomic Approach

by
Stephen Pheasant
Ergonomics Advisor
National Back Pain Association

and

David Stubbs
Robens Institute
University of Surrey

NBPA

National Back Pain Association

First published 1991

Published by
The National Back Pain Association
31-33 Park Road, Teddington, Middlesex, TW11 OAB
Telephone: 081-977-5474

Print and design by Redesign, Bethnal Green, London E2 9PB. Tel: 081-983 1833.

A catalogue record for this publication is available from the British Library.

ISBN 0 9507726 4 X

Contents

Acknowledgements

The lifting procedures described in the section of the present work which deal with 'training' are based extensively upon those described in an earlier NBPA publication called 'Lifting Instructors Manual'. The authors of the present work would like to acknowledge the contribution made by the authors of the earlier work; C.R. Hayne and J.D.G. Troup, and illustrator Don Charlesworth.

The NBPA wishes to thank Thorn EMI UK Rental for their support in financing this publication.

Disclaimer

The risks associated with lifting and handling tasks are complex – and to some extent they are unpredictable. In preparing this text every reasonable attempt has been made to ensure that the advice which is given conforms to what would currently be regarded as 'good working practice'. The reader is warned however that there are no infallible rules in this area and each situation must be judged on its own merits. Neither the authors nor the publisher can accept responsibility for any consequences which might result from decisions made upon the basis of the advice given herein.

Note: For ease of reading, the masculine gender has been used throughout this publication, but all statements apply equally to males and females.

Introduction

Back pain is an extremely common condition. Between two thirds and three quarters of adults will suffer from one or more episodes of back pain during the course of their working lives. At any point in time, about one person in seven will be suffering from back pain.

About thirteen percent of all certified sickness absence in the UK is due to back pain. The figure is climbing steadily and it is climbing more rapidly in women than in men. The annual cost of this sickness absence is thought to be in the order of £3000 million.

Most attacks of back pain clear up within a few weeks at the outside – although a small minority of cases may lead to prolonged periods of disability. Back pain tends to be recurrent; that is, once you have had one attack you are very much more likely to have others. About 50% of people who have time off work because of back problems have another attack within a year; and the likelihood of a recurrence increases with the number of attacks that an individual has.

Some people with long standing back trouble have repeated attacks of pain, which are separated by relatively long periods during which their backs seem to be more or less normal. During these pain free periods they can do quite heavy work without discomfort. Other people find that they have a dull ache in their backs almost all of the time. The discomfort is aggravated by certain characteristic activities and at times it will flare up into episodes of intense pain.

Back pain is equally common in men and women, and it occurs at all ages; but it is particularly common in people whose work involves certain sorts of activities. We call these activities risk factors. In people who are not exposed to these risks, back pain is really quite rare. A person's work may not be the sole cause of their back pain; but it is likely to be a significant contributory factor in very many cases. If we do not do something about those aspects of an individual's working life which are causing their back problems we should not be surprised if these problems are recurrent.

Back pain has been the subject of a great deal of research and although there is much that we do not know about the subject, the sorts of working activities which are likely to place you at risk are reasonably well known. Back pain has been found to be associated with:

- Heavy work – lifting and handling, forceful exertion, bending, twisting etc
- Working in a stooped position
- Prolonged sitting in a fixed position
- Vibration
- Psychological stress

This publication is mainly concerned with lifting and handling. But it is important to realize that the effects of the various activities which lead to back trouble, are likely to be cumulative. The work of a delivery driver, for example, may involve prolonged sitting in a fixed position, with vibration exposure as well as heavy lifting. Similarly, the work of a nurse may require her to spend long time periods in a stooped position and be psychologically stressful, as well as being physically very demanding.

Are some sorts of people more at risk than others, given that they are doing the same kind of work? Since back pain is commonly recurrent, it follows that a person with a history of the condition is likely to be at a higher level of risk. The magnitude of this risk will depend on the extent to which the previous episodes of the condition have left their back vulnerable to further injury; but in practice this may be difficult to determine. Some studies have shown that tall people may be more prone to back trouble than short people, but there is really very

Back Pain at Work

little in it. Some people may be at risk because of the anatomical make-up of their spines, but except for certain relatively rare conditions the effects are again small.

Strength and fitness are very much more important. In general the stronger and fitter you are, the less likely you are to injure your back doing heavy work. Smokers are also more susceptible to back trouble than non-smokers, although we do not really know why. Statistically speaking, your chances of having serious back problems increase by about 20% for every ten cigarettes per day that you smoke. So this is yet another very good reason for giving it up.

Sometimes an attack of back pain comes on suddenly and the individual concerned regards it (rightly or wrongly) as having been caused by the activity they were engaged in at the time. But equally often the condition has an insidious onset and the victim is unable to attribute it to any activity in particular (see Figure 1).

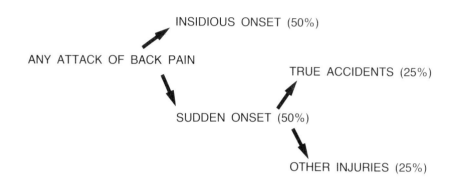

Figure 1

The episodes of sudden onset may be divided, more or less equally, into two further categories. About half are true accidents such as slips and falls; situations where a load gets out of hand and so on. The other half are not really accidents in the strict sense of the word. Although they will often be classed as such for administrative purposes, and in practical terms it is perfectly reasonable that they should. In these cases, the back injury occurs during the course of a normal working activity, performed in what seems to be the ordinary way. Lifting injuries may fall into either category. Some lifting injuries, which do not involve true accidents are obviously attributable to overexertion: the individual overstrains himself trying to shift a load which is beyond his capacity or handling a more modest load in an awkward position. It is also quite common for an attack of back pain to come on as an individual straightens up after a period in a stooped position whether or not he is handling a load at the time.

The fact that an episode of back pain came on gradually, rather than during the course of a specific working activity does not mean that the person's work was not its principal cause. Heavy lifting may result in cumulative damage to the spine over a period of time, leading to an insidious onset of symptoms. That an episode of back pain comes on suddenly, as the individual attempts a particular lifting action, does not mean that it was caused by that particular action alone. The cumulative effects of heavy lifting may leave a person's back in a vulnerable state in which it is susceptible to injury; the point at which the 'injury' occurs may be more or less a matter of chance.

Lifting and Handling Injuries

About one quarter of all certified accidents at work are due to lifting and handling activities. Of these approximately half are back injuries. The remainder involve the hands, feet, arms, legs etc. The sorts of activities relating to these back injuries are very varied and encompass lifting, lowering, holding, carrying, pushing, pulling, throwing. In most types of industrial work, the load will be an inert object, but in other contexts it could be a human being or an animal. In a few cases, the 'load' is an immovable object, like a machine part that is stuck in place or an excessively stiff lever or control.

In seeking to establish safe working practices with regard to lifting and handling tasks it is necessary to consider three principal kinds of risks:

● **the risk of overexertion**
   Due to a load which is beyond the capacity of the individual concerned, given the circumstances under which he is required to lift it

● **the risk of cumulative damage.**
   Due to repetitive lifting, fixed working posture and so on

● **the risk of accidental injury**
   In practice these risks very frequently occur in combination and it may be difficult to separate them in any particular case

In theory there are three possible ways of dealing with these risks:

● *selection*

● *training*

● *ergonomics*

The extent to which the selection of workers is a viable option will depend, in part, upon the state of the labour market. But even where recruitment presents little or no problem, it is still genuinely difficult to determine which individuals are likely to be most at risk in a given situation. Where possible it obviously makes sense to allocate the heaviest jobs to the biggest and strongest people; and to transfer people who are known to be unfit to lighter forms of work. Beyond these fairly simple commonsense precautions, the scope for more sophisticated selection procedures is likely to be limited.

Training has been the most popular approach to dealing with these problems in the past. Training programmes of the conventional kind tend to be based on the assumption that back injuries generally result from faulty lifting technique. There is little real evidence for this belief; and although most people who run training programmes have their own favourite success stories which they like to tell, the evidence available at the present time suggests that successful training programmes are the exception rather than the rule.

There are a number of reasons why this might be the case. It is perfectly true that lifting is generally an unconsidered, unplanned kind of action. We do it automatically without thinking. It is also true that there are often good ways and bad ways of lifting a particular load; or at the least, some ways which are less hazardous than others. The real trouble often comes in situations where the nature of the load or the design of the working environment prevents the individual from lifting in a safe way, however well trained he may be.

Figure 2 illustrates what is generally considered to be a good lifting technique, details of this lift will be examined

Figure 2

7

later. The problem is that it can only be done this way if there is a compact load, an unobstructed work area, and the load is to be lifted within a limited range of heights.

It follows therefore that lifting training can only be effective in the context of an overall strategy for designing safe systems of work – or to be more precise safer systems of work, because the total elimination of risk is generally an unattainable ideal. This is what is meant by the 'ergonomic approach'.

The EC Directive and HSC Guidelines

In May 1990 the Council of the European Community published a Directive on 'The minimum health and safety requirements for the handling of loads where there is a risk, particularly of back injury to workers'. Each European member state will be required to implement this Directive by the end of 1992 and the statutory body responsible for so doing in the UK is the Health and Safety Commission (HSC).

The most recent draft of the forthcoming regulations available at the time of writing, appeared in the form of a Consultative Document in November 1991. In essence, the employer will be required to:

● avoid hazardous manual handling operations where possible

● assess any hazardous handling operations that cannot be avoided

● remove or reduce the risk of injury, using assessment as a basis for action.

The reader who is specifically concerned with meeting these requirements should refer to the Consultative Document (or whatever might have superseded it) for further details. The Consultative Document contains the full text of the EC Directive.

Safe Systems of Work

The first stage of any effective programme for preventing lifting and handling injuries is a thorough investigation of current working practices. This will generally involve both direct observation and discussions with the people involved. It is important to find out about the unofficial short cuts that people take as well as the 'official' way of doing things. Foremen and supervisors sometimes turn a blind eye to these practices in order to get the job done on time. Accident records and sickness absence figures may help to pinpoint areas of high risk.

Accounts of 'near misses', where an accident was narrowly avoided, are another important source of data.

In terms of back pain prevention, the overall objective of this investigation will be to determine those aspects of the working situation which are likely to lead to an unreasonably high level of loading on the person's back. It is necessary to take into account:

● **dynamic loading** due to lifting and handling actions and other vigorous physical activity

● **static loading** due to holding actions, stooped postures and so on

Having identified the most important sources of loading, a coherent plan for dealing with the problem can be made. Some sources of loading can be eliminated by training people to work in a different way. However, many will require changes in the design of the working system. To recognize these options, we need to understand some basic principles of anatomy and body mechanics.

Anatomy

The human spine is a flexible column of 24 bones called vertebrae, plus a larger wedge shaped bone at the bottom, which is called the sacrum (Figure 3). The uppermost vertebra supports the skull and the sacrum articulates with the hip bones at the sacroiliac joints. There are seven cervical vertebrae in the neck. The ribs are attached in pairs to each of the twelve thoracic vertebrae and there are five lumbar vertebrae in the small of the back. Some people actually have four or six lumbar vertebrae, but it does not seem to affect them in any way.

Figure 4

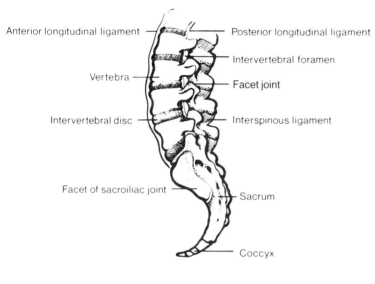

Figure 3

In discussing anatomy and lifting, the lumbar region is the most important area (Figure 4) since although any part of the spine or trunk may be damaged during lifting and handling activities, it is the lumbar spine and its adjacent structures that tend to be damaged most frequently.

Between each pair of vertebrae, both in the lumbar region and elsewhere, is a tough pad of tissue called the intervertebral disc which acts as a shock absorber. The disc has a fibrous outer layer and a fluid filled centre. The fibres of the outer layer are arranged something like the cords of a cross-ply motor car tyre.

Although there is a certain amount of disagreement on the subject, most medical people now believe that only a relatively small minority of back injuries (probably not more than 5%) involve damage to the intervertebral discs. Disc injuries, when they occur, do however, tend to be among the more serious sorts of back problems.

Fractures of the bones of the spine are also quite rare, and almost never occur as a result of lifting actions, except when the bones have been weakened by osteoporosis – for example, in elderly women. The majority of back injuries of the ordinary kind probably involve damage to the muscles and soft tissues which support the spine and control its movements. There may also be a misalignment of the small apophyseal facet joints which lie behind the discs and such problems as the entrapment of nerve roots.

Figure 5

Figure 6

The Lifting Action

Figure 5 shows a man lifting a weight in a stooped position, in which his trunk is more or less horizontal. A very simple mechanical calculation, based upon the principle of levers allows you to appreciate the risk involved in this action. The combined weight (W) of the load and the trunk acts at a distance (x) from the fulcrum of the lumbar spine. (The fulcrum of a lever is the point at which it pivots). This load must be counterbalanced by a force (F) exerted by the back muscles which act at a very much shorter distance (d) from the fulcrum. By the principle of levers:

$$Wx = Fd$$

In practice, this means that the tension in the muscles when lifting a load in this position can be as much as ten times greater than the weight of the load. The long muscles which run down the back have a line of pull which is near enough parallel to the spine, so any tension in these muscles results in an equal and opposite compression (C) on the spine itself. The tension in the muscles, or the compression on the spine, may result in damage.

When lifting heavy weights it is instinctive to hold ones breath and tense the abdominal muscles. This natural protective mechanism puts pressure on the abdominal cavity and thus helps relieve the loading on the spine. This is rather like having a fluid filled cushion for the spine (Figure 6). However, there is a risk that certain regions of the muscular walls of the abdominal cavity can fail under pressure. This is why people who lift heavy weights sometimes suffer from hernias.

Figure 5 shows that the mechanical loading on the spine and its muscles will increase with the following three factors:

● the weight of the load

● the distance of the centre of gravity from the fulcrum of the spine

● the inclination of the trunk

Note that lifting a relatively light load held at arm's length results in the same mechanical loading on the spine and its muscles as lifting a heavier load held closer to the body. Note also that as the trunk tilts forward, its centre of gravity gets further away from the fulcrum of the spine, so the mechanical loading on the spine and its muscles increases.

Stooping to pick up a light object from floor level may expose the spine to a considerable degree of loading by virtue of the weight of the trunk alone.

Static Loading

Static muscle activity such as loading actions and stooped postures is more fatiguing than dynamic muscle activity of similar intensity and it results in a very much greater strain on the heart. Tasks performed with the arms in a raised position are a problem in this respect. Static loading of the intervertebral discs may lead to mechanical 'creep' effects which render them more susceptible to damage. **The elimination of static loading is therefore a high priority in the design of working systems.**

Important sources of static loading, which should be avoided wherever possible, include:

● working with the arms in a raised position

● working with the trunk in an inclined position (either forwards or to the sides)

- holding actions in which the person supports the weight of an object or holds it steady against the work piece

- struggling to lift objects which are too heavy to be moved smoothly or easily or which are stuck in place

Bending and Twisting

The action of bending down to pick up an object from close to floor level has two components to it. The trunk as a whole tilts forward at the hips and the spine flexes upon itself, particularly in the lumbar region, ie the back tends to become more rounded. As the lumbar spine flexes, the muscles and soft tissues come under tension and the discs are deformed. Thus the flexed spine is susceptible to damage at relatively low levels of mechanical loading.

Twisting actions are particularly hazardous, partly because of the patterns of muscle activity involved and partly because they also entail deformation of the discs. To a lesser extent this is also true for side bending actions.

The worst combination is probably a lift from floor level, involving a bending and twisting action, with the arms outstretched, after a period of working in a stooped position. Such actions are surprisingly common.

Foot Placement

Correct foot placement is in many respects the key to safe lifting. This is partly a matter of training in correct technique, and partly a matter of the layout of the working area.

The strength of the lifting action is greatest when the line of thrust lies within the area of a person's footbase. This is represented as the shaded area in Figure 7. Lifting strength falls off rapidly as the load moves outside this area. In part this may be due to the increased loading on the back and shoulder muscles, but it is also a matter of balance.

Figure 7

When lifting a load outside the limits of the footbase, an individual has to use the weight of the body to counterbalance the weight of the load. If the individual slips or loses their footing, or if the load moves in an unpredictable fashion, he may suddenly find himself off balance in a way that he is unable to correct; or he may over-strain himself in trying to regain his balance.

When lifting a load outside the area of stability determined by the footbase, the individual is potentially out of balance and therefore at risk. The elimination of obstacles to optimal foot placement is therefore a high priority in the ergonomics of lifting and handling.

It may not always be possible to achieve this in practice. A lifting action which commences at a distance and moves into the **footbase** ie towards the body, is probably preferable to one which commences in the footbase and terminates at a distance, since in the former case, the body is moving into balance and towards the area of greatest strength. But neither is desirable.

Ergonomics

An ergonomic assessment of a working system, in which people handle loads manually, would generally involve consideration of:

● the task – the actions performed, the overall workload, rest pauses etc

● the load – weight, bulk, stability etc

● the environment – work space layout, working conditions etc

● the personnel – age, sex, strength, fitness etc

The Working Area

In thinking about the ergonomics of lifting and handling tasks, it is often useful to divide up the area which surrounds the working person into vertical height ranges. It is easiest to describe these by referring to the levels of various parts of the person's body in a relaxed standing position, knee height, elbow height, shoulder height and so on. These levels will of course vary considerably between individuals, as shown in Figure 8.

The strength of the lifting action is greatest at around knuckle height, as measured with the hands hanging by the sides. On average this is about 75 cm (or 30 ins) above the floor. The preferred height for lifting and handling tasks extends from knuckle height to elbow height or thereabouts.

The zones on either side of the preferred range, from elbow height to shoulder height and from knuckle height to knee height are somewhat less satisfactory, but acceptable provided the load is within reasonable limits. Lifting actions below knee height or above shoulder height should be avoided where possible, unless the weight of load is low.

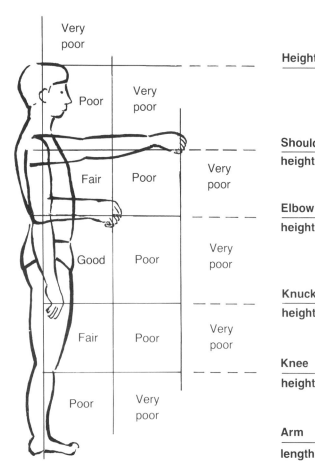

Figure 8

	Men			Women		
	Short	Ave	Tall	Short	Ave	Tall
Height	165	177	188	153	164	174
Shoulder height	134	145	156	124	134	143
Elbow height	103	112	121	96	103	111
Knuckle height	72	78	85	69	75	81
Knee height	52	57	62	48	53	57
Arm length	64	69	74	58	63	68

Source: Pheasant (1986, 1991)

All dimensions in cm.

Lifts which commence in the lower part of the overall height range and continue into the upper part, pose a particular problem. Somewhere just above elbow height a change of grip will be required. Alternatively, the lifter will have to raise the elbows out sideways and lean backwards, thus risking a loss of balance. Both manoeuvres are hazardous.

For the purposes of argument each vertical height zone can be divided into three parts, as shown in Figure 8. Lifting actions performed at more than about half arm's length can only be regarded as acceptable if the weight is low. Lifting actions at more than arm's length should be avoided altogether, unless the weight is **very low**.

The Load

What is a safe load? This question has no easy answer. At the very least it will depend upon the circumstances. A person whose back is in a vulnerable state may be at risk when handling loads which would be well within the safe capacity of a normally fit person. Unfortunately, the warning signs of an impending attack of back pain are not always apparent – either to the individual concerned or to anybody else. In practice therefore, it will be difficult or impossible to guard against this sort of risk.

In many respects, the best guide as to whether a particular load should be regarded as too heavy to handle, is the sensation of effort entailed for the individual concerned. If a load feels too heavy, then it probably is too heavy. Similarly, if you find that a particular lifting or carrying task makes you feel unduly fatigued or out of breath, then this is a good indication that it is beyond your capacity.

In general a **bulky** load will tend to be both **more difficult** and **more hazardous** to handle than a **compact** load of the same weight. The centre of gravity of the bulky load will be further from the lifter's body. So it will both have a greater leverage about the fulcrum of the spine, and be more likely to put the lifter out of balance. Wide and long loads may pose particular handling problems; as may loads which are unstable or difficult to grip. The level of risk involved in handling a particular load will also depend upon things like obstructions in the working area which limit foot placement, the height range of the lift and so on.

For a number of reasons therefore, it is genuinely difficult to be specific about the weight of load which is acceptable in a given situation. But very often this is the wrong way of looking at the problem. Instead, one should be asking whether the working system as a whole is ergonomically satisfactory; that is, does it conform to what is generally regarded as good practice in methods of manual handling.

However, there clearly does come a point at which a load is too heavy, given the nature of the situation in which you are handling it. The guidelines given in the following section might be a useful starting point in considering these questions. But it must be stressed that they are intended as a rough guide only; and in practice it is necessary to evaluate each situation on its own merits. **The bottom line is that there is no such thing as a safe load.**

In practice, the tasks which are most difficult to assess are often ones which involve the frequent handling of relatively light loads. Although each individual effort may be harmless in itself, the cumulative effect of repeated bending, twisting or lifting actions may be considerable, particularly if they are combined with a high static workload.

Guidelines Concerning Load Weight

The following guidelines are based on the November 1991 HSC Consultative Document – in an appendix of which is found a figure similar to Figure 8 of the present text. But rather than having a verbal description of each vertical and horizontal lifting zone it has *guideline weights* in kilograms.

These guideline weights are shown in Table 1. They are considered to define a boundary, beyond which the risk of injury is sufficiently great to warrant a more detailed assessment of the system of work. It is noted however, that even where manual handling tasks fall within these limits, they should still be eliminated or improved where it is reasonably practicable to do so; and it is also noted that the limits may be exceeded *"where a more detailed assessment shows that it is safe to do so".*

Table 1: **Guideline Weights**

Height Range	Less than half arm's length Kg	Between half arm's length and full arm's length Kg
Below knee height	10	5
Knee height – knuckle height	20	10
Knuckle height – elbow height	25	15
Elbow height – shoulder height	20	10
Shoulder height – full height	10	5

Source: Health and Safety Commission (1991) pp 56

The guideline weights given in Table 1 are for lifts performed less than once per minute, under relatively favourable conditions – a compact stable load which is easy to grasp, with an upright non-twisted trunk, unobstructed workspace, satisfactory environmental conditions and so on. Under these circumstances, the guideline figures are held to *"give reasonable protection to nearly all men and between one half and two thirds of women. To provide the same degree of protection to women, the guideline figures should be reduced by about one third."* It is also noted that *"even for a minority of fit well-trained individuals working under favourable conditions, the guideline figures should not normally be exceeded by a factor of more than about two."*

It might be useful to think of the guideline figures as a benchmark defining a notional boundary of risk. This benchmark may need to be shifted downwards for some people – for example the less able half of the female working population, elderly workers and so on. At a level of loading equivalent to about twice the guideline figure is another benchmark beyond which the level of risk might be considered unacceptably high. Between the upper and lower benchmarks, lies a region in which a steadily increasing number of people are exposed to a steadily increasing degree of risk. (At least this is the present authors' interpretation of the matter.)

The Consultative Document also suggests that the guideline weights should be reduced, if the lift involves stooping or twisting. It provides correction factors for both of these movements. These are summarized in Table 2.

Table 2 : **Correction Factors for Stooping and Twisting**

Reduce the guideline weights by the percentages shown.		
Stooping	20°	25%
	45°	35%
	90°	50%

Twisting	30°	10%
	60°	15%
	90°	20%

Source: Health and Safety Commission (1991) pp 34-35

It is also noted that the load which a team of two or more lifters can handle safely is less than the sum of the individual capacities of the members of the team. For a two person team the safe capacity is approximately two thirds of the sum of their individual capacities; for a three person team the safe capacity is approximately half the sum of their individual capacities. If slopes or steps are to be negotiated, the capacity is diminished further.

Rest Pauses

Rest pauses are important for recovery from muscular fatigue. Again it is difficult to be specific but the following rules of thumb are worth bearing in mind:

- frequent short pauses tend to be more beneficial than infrequent long pauses

- the time required for recovery will be less if the individual concerned takes a rest before the sensations of fatigue become pronounced

- it is always a bad idea to work on to the point of exhaustion.

Lifting and Handling Tasks: A RISK ASSESSMENT CHECKLIST

© Stephen Pheasant and David Stubbs

This checklist is intended as an aid to the evaluation of working practices. An answer of YES to any of these questions indicates a potential problem area.

The Task

1. Does the overall physical workload seem unreasonably heavy, considering the strength and fitness of the workforce?

2. Does the task require a weaker person to exert himself to the limit of his strength?

> 2.1 Lifting?
> 2.2 Pushing?
> 2.3 Pulling?
> 2.4 Other?

3. Does the task require the person to support a load or exert a sustained force for more than a short period?

> 3.1 Lifting?
> 3.2 Pushing?
> 3.3 Pulling?
> 3.4 Carrying?
> 3.5 Other?

4. Does the lifting action commence in an unsatisfactory position?

> 4.1 Does the lifter bend from the waist/hips?
> 4.2 Does the lifter twist the trunk?
> 4.3 Does the lifter lean over or reach out sideways?

5. Is the lifting action performed outside the range of heights which is acceptable, given the nature of the load?

> 5.1 Is it necessary to lift above shoulder height?
> 5.2 Is it necessary to lift below knee height?
> 5.3 Is it necessary to make awkward movements to complete the lift?
> 5.4 Is it necessary to handle heavy or difficult loads outside the preferred range of heights (ie from knuckle height to elbow height)?

6. Does the lifting action involve potentially hazardous movements?

> 6.1 A turning motion?
> 6.2 A sidestepping motion?
> 6.3 A change of grip?

7. Does the task require reaching actions which are beyond the capacity of a short person?

8. Is it necessary to work for long periods in an unsatisfactory posture?

> 8.1 In a stooped position?
> 8.2 In a crouching position?
> 8.3 With the hands above mid-torso height?
> 8.4 In a twisted position?
> 8.5 In an asymmetric or side bending position?
> 8.6 Do the demands of the task prevent the worker from changing position at will?
> 8.7 Is the worker required to take their weight on one leg?

9. Are repetition rates unreasonably high?

> 9.1 Is it necessary to perform more than 10 handling actions per minute?
> 9.2 Is it necessary to handle heavy loads more than once per minute?

10. Does the person work continuously without adequate rest periods?

11. Does the person perform the same task continuously throughout the working day?

The Load

12. Does the weight of the load seem unreasonably heavy, considering the nature of the task and the strength and fitness of the workforce?
(See page 13.)

13. Is the load difficult to handle?

13.1 Is it too bulky?
13.2 Is it too long?
13.3 Is it too wide?
13.4 Is it difficult to grip firmly?
13.5 Is it unstable?
13.6 Are its contents likely to shift during movement?
13.7 Does it have sharp edges, splinters etc.
13.8 Can it trap the fingers?
13.9 Does it obstruct the person's vision?
13.10 Is it hazardous or offensive in some other way?

14. Is it difficult for the person to obtain assistance when handling difficult or heavy loads?

15. Could the person's task be made easier or safer by marking or labelling the load in some way?

15.1 Weight?
15.2 Heavy end?
15.3 Contents?
15.4 Handling procedures?

The Environment

16. Are there obstructions in the working area which will prevent the worker from keeping the load close to the body throughout the lift?

16.1 Is it necessary to reach over obstructions?
16.2 Is it necessary to reach into containers?
16.3 Is the worker free to adopt the most advantageous foot placements?
16.4 Are heavy or frequently used objects stored in inaccessible places?

17. Are there obstacles or hazards in the working area?

17.1 Things to bump into?
17.2 Things to trip over?
17.3 Steps or changes of level?
17.4 Is the floor slippery?
17.5 Does the floor need cleaning?
17.6 Is there rubbish or clutter that needs clearing up?

18. Are there problems of access or clearance for a tall or bulky person?

18.1 Headroom?
18.2 Passageways between obstacles?
18.3 Legroom under working surfaces (for sitting people)?
18.4 Toe recesses under working surfaces (for standing people)?

19. Are there environmental problems?

19.1 Lighting levels?
19.2 Heat?
19.3 Humidity?
19.4 Cold?
19.5 Wind?
19.6 Ventilation?
19.7 Dust?
19.8 Noise?

The Person

20. Are any workers who are carrying out manual handling tasks,

20.1 Less than 18 years?
20.2 Greater than 55 years?

21. Do any workers have

21.1 Limited range of motion in limbs and/or back?
21.2 Heart or respiratory problems?
21.3 Any history or hernias?
21.4 Any musculoskeletal disorder especially a previous history of back pain?
21.5 Temporary impairment or debility?

22. Are any workers pregnant?

23. Does any worker have specific difficulties in carrying out the manual handling tasks allotted to them?

24. Are there problems with regard to clothing or personal equipment?

24.1 Does the clothing hamper or constrain the worker's movements?
24.2 Are there items of safety clothing which are
(a) Required but not readily available?
(b) Readily available but not appropriate?
(c) Both readily available and appropriate but not used?
24.3 Gloves?
24.4 Boots?
24.5 Headgear?
24.6 Eye protection?
24.7 Other?

25. Is there anything else which makes the task more difficult or hazardous than it needs to be?

Having analysed and evaluated existing working practices, one is in a position to decide upon the most effective course of action to remedy the problems which they pose.

For example, is it possible to solve the problem

● by changing the layout of the working area so as to allow people to work in a better way?

● by redesigning the load so as to make it easier to handle?

● by providing mechanical lifting aids of some kind?

● by allocating more people to the job so as to reduce the overall burden on each person?

● by training the workforce in safer working practices?

Alternatively, can the working system be redesigned so as to eliminate the need for handling the load altogether?

The content of a typical training course could be divided into three areas:

● knowledge

● procedures and practices

● skills

In practice, these may be mixed up together in various combinations. But the distinctions between these components are worth bearing in mind because they pose different sorts of training problems. It is also worth distinguishing between safety training as such, and safety propaganda. The former is concerned with the imparting of information and the acquisition of skill; the latter is concerned with persuading people to make use of skills and knowledge they already have and to follow correct working procedures.

A certain amount of background knowledge concerning anatomy, body mechanics and so on helps to put the practical content of a training course into context. The way this is taught needs to be carefully matched to the audience. For example, the requirements of a group of office workers would be different from those of a group of engineers. The knowledge element in a course can be taught in a 'classroom' type of environment, although practical demonstrations are always an advantage. But the procedures and skills of lifting should really be taught in the working environment under realistic working conditions, and using the sorts of loads which will be handled on the job.

The distinction between skills and procedures is often blurred; but it has important consequences nevertheless. An individual may be familiar with correct procedures for lifting a certain kind of load, but be unskilled in its execution. and conversely, may become skilled in unsafe working practices. Failure to comply with correct procedures may sometimes be overcome by persuasion in one form or another. But lack of skill cannot be overcome by these means. Skills are sometimes taught as if they are procedures – 'doing it by numbers'. Some skills can be acquired in this way, at least in the early stages. But the execution of a smoothly coordinated lifting action is a skill which requires practice; and coaching by an experienced trainer who has the ability to identify and correct bad habits. This is no easy matter.

It is sometimes said that we remember:
   10% of what we **read**
   20% of what we **hear**
   30% of what we **see**
   50% of what we **see and hear**
   and
   70% of what we **do for ourselves**

Posters and leaflets may be useful adjuncts to safety training, particularly on a propaganda basis to encourage compliance with procedures. They are, however no substitute for participative programmes of learning by doing, involving discussions of practical problems and 'hands on' exercises in the working situation.

The training session can thus become a collaborative exercise in problem solving in which the trainer learns from the students as well as the other way around, both bringing their own areas of knowledge and expertise to the learning situation. In this way, the trainer can gain valuable insights into current working practices which can be carried forward into subsequent ergonomic improvements.

Training

Dressing for Work

Students should be advised to attend the training session wearing old loosely fitting clothing which will not hamper their movements. Women in particular should be reminded to wear 'sensible' shoes and not to wear short or tight skirts. Tracksuits or boiler suits are probably best of all.

The Basic Lift

The lift shown in Figure 9 is generally considered to be the foundation of good lifting technique, although in practice its applications are limited.

Figure 9

The basic lift should be practised initially using a box like load which is not more than about 30 cm square and which is heavy enough to involve some sensation of effort, but not so heavy as to tire if it is lifted twenty or thirty times during a practice session. Around 5 kg is probably about right for most people. In the first instance, the load should be lifted from the floor on to a low bench or table. As an aid to learning, the lift can be taught in the following stages, but the overall aim should be to achieve a well co-ordinated, easy and natural pattern of movement, rather than attempting to follow a self-conscious lifting drill which has been learned by rote.

1. **Foot placement:** Start with the load between the feet The leading foot should be in line with the side of the box, pointing in the direction of movement, with the toes level with the front edge of the box.

2. **Knees bent/back straight:** Get down to the level of the load by bending the knees and hips Tuck the chin in, and keep the back straight 'from head to tail'. Lean forward a bit to get over the load, but do not incline the trunk more than is absolutely necessary. Avoid putting one knee on the floor, this makes for an unstable lifting action. Deep knee bends may also be a problem. They can place an excessive strain on the knee joints and on the thigh muscles which straighten the leg. People with knee problems or weak thigh muscles may find it difficult to lift correctly for this reason.

3. **Grip:** It is important to get a full firm, secure grip on the load. Loads which are handled frequently should be designed with this in mind. Grip the box at the upper outer corner on the side of the leading foot, tilt it slightly and grip the opposite corner with the other hand. Other hand placements may be better in some cases, depending on what is to be done with the load.

4. **Lift:** Move the load by leaning forward over it a little, keeping the rear arm straight. Pull the box firmly into contact with the body, moving the rear hand forward along the lower edge of the box. Stand up in one co-ordinated movement, keeping the load in contact with the body throughout.

5. **Lowering:** To lower the load, reverse the procedure bending the hips and knees, whilst tilting the load to avoid trapping the fingers.

Varying the Load

When the trainees have mastered the basic lifting actions on a compact and easily handled load, they can then start to experiment with more difficult loads. For this purpose it may be useful to have a range of boxes of up to 60 cm square and weighing up to 25 kg. **Each individual trainee must learn to recognize the limits of their strength and lifting capacity, so as to avoid those situations in which they may be at risk of overexertion.** The remainder of the training course should be based upon those type of loads which the trainee is likely to encounter in their everyday work. Procedures for lifting a number of commonly encountered 'difficult loads' are described below.

Using Body Weight

Many lifting instructions talk about 'using body weight' to move the load. This is said to 'take the effort out of work'. Earlier it was noted that body weight must be used as a counterbalance when lifting outside the footbase. But the idea that body weight can be used to actually lift a load is somewhat confusing. It is sometimes possible however, to move a load horizontally by using its own momentum, having first got it moving by using the body's own momentum. Having done so, it may be possible to swing the load upward with relatively little effort. Tricks like this take practice and they can only be employed usefully on relatively light loads.

● **Above all, lift the load smoothly – don't be a jerk**

The Ergonomic Approach

The ergonomic approach to safe lifting is applicable both to the design of working procedures which will be performed on a regular basis and to the minimization of risk in the performance of 'one off' lifting and handling tasks. In the latter case, trainees must learn to plan their own working activities according to good ergonomic principles. For example:

● Is the working area clear and free from obstructions?

● Can the load be modified in some way to make it easier to lift?

● Can the load be turned around so that the 'heavy side' (ie. centre of gravity) is close to the body?

● Can the lift be carried through to completion without interruption?

● Would it help to use a trestle or platform as a half way stage?

● How many people are required to lift the load safely?

● Would it be better to put the load on a trolley or in a wheelbarrow or to use some other kind of mechanical aid?

In general:

● **Stop, think, lift**

Teamwork

The lifting of loads by two or more people presents its own particular set of risks. In general these risks will be minimized if the members of the team are well matched for height and if one person acts as 'team leader' using a predetermined set of commands such as 'ready, steady, lift' etc.

In team lifting it is also important that the people concerned should have sufficient space to manoeuvre as a group, sufficient handholds on the load and so on. This may necessitate putting the load on a stretcher or sling etc.

Handling Sacks

The preferred method for sack handling will depend on its size, weight and carrying distance. Light sacks (less than about 20 kg or 44 lbs) may be carried for short distances on the shoulder or clasped in front of the body. For heavier sacks or longer distances a sack trolley is preferable. In applying the following lifting procedures remember what has previously been said about 'safe loads'.

(i) **Lifting from the floor** (Figure 10)

The underlying principles are the same as those previously described for the basic lift. Stand at the end of the sack that is easiest to grip. Take up the starting position for the basic lift; grasp the end of the sack, and leaning forward, set it upright. Now reposition the feet and change grip. One hand clasps the sack against the body and the other is placed below it. To raise the sack on to the shoulder, a lifting platform can be used as an intermediate stage. This allows the hands and feet to be re-positioned and gives a more comfortable starting position for the second part of the lift. Reposition the feet and change the grip. Set the sack upright and bend the knees and hips to get it on to the shoulder.

Figure 10

Figure 11

(ii) **Lifting and carrying from platform or lorry** (Figure 11).

The sack is held at the top, the knees bent and sack tilted forward to take the weight. Then in one smooth movement straighten the legs and move off.

(iii) **Carrying sacks on the shoulders**

If not too heavy, a sack can be carried on one shoulder. But the bulkier it is, or the longer the carry distance, the more tiring it will be for the neck, shoulder and arm muscles. People who habitually carry loads on their shoulders are liable to suffer from neck problems, which is a good argument for using a sack trolley or some other form of transport. When carrying on the shoulder, it is best to start from a platform. Stand with the back to the platform, ease the sack on to the shoulder, bending the knees before taking the weight. The sequence for lowering is the reverse of lifting. Lower the sack from the shoulder to the platform, or if safe to do so, ease it off the shoulder and drop it. If the sack has to be lowered under control, bend the hips and knees, and slide it back off the shoulders.

(iv) **Two person lift** (Figure 12)

The principles are again similar to those of the basic lift. Two people stand on either side of the sack, which is first set upright. The outer foot is the leading foot and points in the direction of movement. The leading hand takes the upper corner of the sack. Be sure that only one of the pair gives the word of command. To obtain a better grip, especially for big sacks, a strong wooden or metal bar, slightly longer than the width of the sack, may be placed underneath it.

Figure 12

Long Loads

Long loads present special handling problems. They are less easy to control than compact loads and weight for weight they therefore pose a greater level of risk. Particular problems may arise with long loads which can bend in the middle – like carpets or planks of wood.

(i) **One person lift** (Figure 13)

The stages of this procedure are similar to those described for sacks. First use the basic lift technique to up-end the load. Then lift it on to the platform, keeping it in a vertical position, as close as possible to the body. Raise the load to the shoulder, by bending the knees, until the shoulder is level with the point of balance of the load. Then carry the load horizontally balanced on the shoulder. Alternatively, carry the load by hugging it to the chest.

If the load is too long or too heavy to handle in this way, get help. If no help is available, it may be possible to raise one end of the load and drag it along the ground.

Figure 13

(ii) **Two person and Team lifting** (Figure 14)

Two people lifting a long load should start at the heavy end. Using the basic lift technique they raise the load in two stages; firstly to hip height; then, having changed grip to shoulder height one person supports this end of the load on his shoulder. The other person goes to the opposite (lighter) end and lifts it on to the shoulder in two stages, using a platform. As in all team lifting, good timing is essential.

Some long loads need to be carried in teams of more than two. Ideally the members of these teams should be as similar in height as possible. Alternatively, the tallest person should be at one end, with the others spaced at suitable distances along the load. Or the load can be handled using slings, with the team members in pairs along its length. The sling passes over the opposite shoulder and is held in both hands. But when loads are this difficult, it will generally be better to transport them on a trolley, or some other kind of wheeled conveyance.

Figure 14

Drums and Barrels

Drums and barrels present particular hazards and should not be handled by the uninitiated. Some can weigh over 250 kg and once on the move they are a menace to life, limb and property. Because of this, no advice is offered here except to urge caution and the need to find alternative safer systems of work.

Sheet Material (Figure 15)

Single handed lifting and carrying of sheet material is an inherently hazardous activity. It necessarily involves twisting; and when outdoors, a strong wind can cause the load to act like a sail. The safest, and usually the quickest way therefore, is for two people to handle the sheet. If only one person is available, the sheet should not be longer than the arm span. Tip the sheet up on to one corner, grasp it safely and keeping the head and back as straight as possible, lift it. Sheet materials which have dangerous or fragile corners should be protected. This is particularly important for glass. Gloves and carrying tools should be used.

Figure 15

Pushing and Pulling (Figure 16)

The strength of a pushing or pulling action depends on foot placement and on the conditions underfoot. Some research findings seem to indicate that, for a given amount of horizontal force, pushing results in a higher level of spinal loading than pulling. Pushing actions can also fix the rib cage, making breathing more difficult. All else being equal, pulling is therefore probably preferable to pushing, although pushing will obviously be safer if there is a possibility of the load getting out of control. Loads on wheels may be a problem on slopes – it is safer to be above the load rather than below it. The best way of shifting a heavy load on the flat, is to put the back against it and push it, using the strong muscles of the legs and thighs – but the problem with this method is that you cannot see where you are going.

Figure 16

Carrying

Carrying involves static muscle loading. Carrying tasks may therefore lead to the rapid onset of muscular fatigue involving the back, shoulder, arm or hand muscles – depending on how the load is supported. Weight for weight, a load carried on the back or shoulders results in a lower level of spinal loading than one carried in front of the body. And a single heavy load carried in one hand will result in a more rapid onset of fatigue, particularly in the shoulder, arm and hand muscles, than two lighter loads carried one in each hand. The onset of fatigue may be delayed by changing hands frequently. In order to minimize the levels of muscular fatigue which result from carrying loads, the following points are recommended:

- use mechanical aids wherever possible

- keep loads light. If possible divide large and heavy loads up into smaller and lighter ones even if this means making more return trips

- minimize the distance. A series of short return trips is preferable to one long carry

- take regular and frequent rest breaks

Mechanical Lifting Aids

Having identified potential problem areas using the risk assessment checklist described earlier, tasks may be redesigned or mechanized in order to reduce or eliminate their inherent hazards. One way of doing this is by the provision of lifting aids such as:

1. Levers can be fitted to the load to increase the mechanical advantage of the lifting action – for oil drums, gas cylinders, manhole covers etc.
2. Handles can be fitted to the load to make it easier to grip – such as hooks, slings etc.
3. Wheels may be fitted to the load to make it easier to transport – such as sack trolleys, luggage trolleys, wheelbarrows etc.
4. Platforms or trestles may be provided to allow the load to be handled at the most convenient height. These must be stable and structurally capable of bearing the load.
5. Other more complex mechanical aids include: palletizers, fork lift trucks, conveyors, cranes and hoists. These and similar aids can be very effective in reducing the physical hazards of manual handling, but other safety problems can arise if insufficient thought is given to their installation and use. For example, fork lift truck operators require training, and vehicle movements around the shop floor and work areas require careful planning to avoid accidents and injuries to operators and pedestrians alike.

Similarly conveyors must be guarded against mechanical entrapment, and maintenance considerations of systems, especially space and access, are essential to ensure safe and continuous operation. Additionally, conveyor speed must be considered as this will dictate the pace of the work whether loading or unloading.

In selecting either a simple or a more complex aid to lifting and handling consider the following questions. Does it:

- reduce the level of hazard?

- reduce the level of physical stress?

- create a new hazard?

- meet the approval of the workforce?

- operate over the full range of conditions where its use is planned?

- prolong the time taken to complete the operation?

- accommodate the gloved hand?

- require training in its use?

- offer the potential for abuse?

These are some of the issues that should be discussed as part of the participative approach to devising safer working systems for lifting and handling loads.

Official Publications

Council of Ministers of the European Community (1991).
Council Directive on the Minimum Health and Safety Requirements for the Manual Handling of Loads where there is a Risk Particularly of Back Injury to Workers. Fourth Individual Directive within the meaning of Article 16 (1) of Directive 89/39/EEC, 90/269/EEC, Official Journal of the European Communities 21.6.90, No L 156/9-13, Brussels.

Health and Safety Commission (1991). *Manual Handling of Loads. Proposals for Regulations and Guidance.* Consultative Document CD36, Health and Safety Executive, London.

Books

Buckle, P (1987). *Musculoskeletal Disorders at Work.* Taylor and Francis, London.

Pheasant, ST (1986). *Bodyspace – Anthropometry, Ergonomics and Design.* Taylor and Francis, London.

Pheasant, ST (1991). *Ergonomics, Work and Health.* Macmillan, London.

Troup, JDG and Edwards, FC (1985). *Manual Handling and Lifting. An Information and Literature Review with Special Reference to the Back.* The Health and Safety Executive, HMSO, London.

Index